SHIRE NATURAL H

C000002333

THE REDSHANK

W. G. HALE

CONTENTS

Cover: *A British Redshank settling on eggs.*

Series editor: Jim Flegg.

Set in 9 point Times roman and printed in Great Britain by C. I. Thomas & Sons
(Haverfordwest) Ltd, Press Buildings, Merlins Bridge, Haverfordwest, Dyfed.

Introduction

On the shore or on the breeding ground, the Redshank (*Tringa totanus*) is perhaps best known for the clamour it makes when disturbed. Springing from some marshy creek or water meadow, it rises yelping into the air to alarm any other birds in the area, and on innumerable occasions it must have frustrated wild-fowlers and birdwatchers alike. It is not without justification that it has been nicknamed 'the warden of the marshes': wherever the Redshank goes it makes its presence felt. As a result it is not the most popular of birds and there are few bird-watchers who can accurately describe a Redshank, despite the fact that it is one of the easiest birds to identify. It is perhaps the most badly illustrated of our common birds, as at the nest it gives the photographer very little time to take a shot before it disappears into its nesting tuft; even the best bird painters have been less than accurate in depicting its plumage. Few have noticed the great variety of plumage that British Red-shanks possess and most texts do not even refer to it.

Larks and Nightingales may be the stuff of literary springs, but they are no competition for the Curlews and Red-shanks on the moorland of east Lanca-shire. The variety of the Redshank's calls, its graceful display flight and its elegant courtship catch and hold the attention of those who come to watch. On a windy day on the mudflats the Redshank is a nondescript brown bird; in the spring sunlight its red legs stand out and, as it raises its wings, the broad white wing bar, the white underside of the wing and the white rump are unmistakable characteristics. Its long bill, its bobbing (so increasing parallax) to determine the distance away of an intruder and its plaintive 'teu-hu-hu' as it takes flight all make it difficult to confuse a Redshank with any other species. Its nearest rela-tions in Europe, the Greenshank (*Tringa nebularia*) and Spotted Redshank (*T.*

erythropus), are superficially similar, but the Redshank's white wing bar makes it easily separable as soon as it is airborne.

Display and courtship

At the end of the winter, Redshanks return to their breeding areas; in the British Isles this is often no great dis-tance. The journey may be of only a few miles, though some birds may travel from as far south as North Africa. They arrive on their breeding grounds earlier than their Icelandic or Scandinavian relations but at much the same time as the popula-tions that breed on the southern North Sea coasts of continental Europe. Old birds may arrive paired, but many arrive singly, some having lost their mates and others to mate for the first time. By the middle of March many birds are haunting their breeding fields and, as the weeks go on, their displays are as graceful and attractive as any in the bird world.

In 1912 Julian Huxley gave an elegant description of the courtship of the Red-shank, which has been much quoted, but he did not have the advantage of watch-ing marked birds and knowing which was male and female. It is not always easy to tell with Redshanks, for their plumage is identical and, when the birds themselves have difficulties, the watcher can hardly be blamed for mistaking a reluctant female for a fighting male, or a bird with which another attempts to copulate for a female. Early in the season the observer is easily confused by enthusiastic male Redshanks and reluctant females, as males try to copulate with other males, and females fight aggressively to dis-courage over-amorous males.

DISPLAY FLIGHT

The first necessity for an unpaired male Redshank on returning to the breeding area is to find a mate; he has an elaborate mechanism for so doing. In ordinary flight he is a graceful bird; in the display flight he is a ballet dancer! Rising from the ground or a suitable perch on a wall or fence, he climbs steeply until he reaches some 40 metres (130 feet) from the ground. After flying horizontally for a short distance, he sets his wings at an angle below the horizontal, displaying his white rump and large white wing bars, and in this position appears to vibrate his wings below the horizontal. This causes him to rise slightly; then, setting his wings, he glides down calling a plaintive 'teuoo-teuoo-teuoo-teuoo' all the time. Again he vibrates his wings and rises gracefully, performing an undulating, switchback flight, high in the air. Throughout his display his head is raised and his tail fanned and in this way he may continue for a distance of up to 1 km (half a mile) or for a time of about four minutes. At the beginning of the breeding season the male's flight is often imperfect: his tail may not be fanned nor his head raised, but with practice he eventually lures a female into the air to see his white rump and wing bars. This is the first move in the establishment of the pair: after the female has followed the male for a distance they both glide down to the ground, trilling.

The display flight of the male may be initiated in several different ways. It can begin in normal flight when the male is alone, when a male is disturbed or when a female passes. A male may begin a display flight during the performance of another, it may occur on a pair meeting or, later in the breeding season, as a distraction display, at low level (3 to 4 metres, 10 to 13 feet), in the presence of a potential predator.

Whilst display flights might take place within a few hundred metres of the future nest site, they may end over a kilometre (half a mile) away and they are in no way territorial. Several males may perform in the air at once and their flight paths criss-cross, or in estuarine habitats they may occur way out over the mudflats. Once a female is attracted into the air, pair formation is likely to follow and thereafter the two birds will spend much time together and eventually copulate and nest.

It is likely that all new pairs of Redshanks are formed during a display flight but some birds arrive on the breeding grounds paired and others meet their mate of the previous year without such ceremony. For young birds, however, the display flight has an important function in the initial formation of the pair.

Following the successful display, where a female has joined the male, after alighting they retain their wings vertically above their backs and continue trilling. Wing-lifting is a common posture in both plovers and sandpipers, and in the Redshank it has been developed into a ceremony which is distinct from the courtship display. After the display flight, Redshanks may glide on depressed wings, trilling; this may be followed by alighting, wing-lifting and continued trilling. On other occasions, one bird will alight in this way, stimulating wing-lifting and trilling in its mate on the ground. This alighting ceremony seems to form a greeting whenever a pair meets away from the nest; it does not occur near the nest nor after the chicks have hatched. The ceremony seems to function to maintain the pair: 45.6 per cent of Redshanks on the Ribble Estuary National Nature Reserve retain their mates in the year subsequent to being marked. Only 6.9 per cent separate and obtain new mates whilst both of the pair are still alive; in 29.8 per cent of the previous year's pairs only the male returns and in 17.7 per cent only the female.

COURTSHIP DISPLAY

Full courtship displays take place only between the members of a pair, though early in the year, in late February and early March, spasmodic attempts at displays by males may be seen on the shore. Males come into breeding condition before females and in the early breeding season they attempt copulation before the females are either paired or ready. There are three major phases to the courtship display: the ground chase, the scraping ceremony and the wing-lifting ceremony. In initial displays males chase females, which often fly away, but occasionally they will stop and fight the males (behaviour which has in the past been interpreted as territorial fighting between males). The chased bird is always a female and the chasing bird a male.

In the chase proper, the male fans his tail and begins the chase, head down and

3

1. *Male Redshank beginning the chase.*

2. *Female Redshank tilting towards the male during the chase.*

3. *Female Redshank (colour-ringed) in full flight from the male.*
4. *Male in wing-lifting posture uttering the 'cacacacaca' note or rattle, immediately prior to attempting copulation.*

with what Huxley described as 'rather the action of a fast-trotting horse'. In the female the body is tilted forward, the head withdrawn and the whole body, bill to tail, held parallel with the ground. The male's feathers are fluffed and sometimes the wings drooped, so that the white rump is visible. The wing nearest the female droops the most and the fanned tail is tilted towards the female as the male runs a metre behind, and to the side, in a strange sideways motion, reminiscent of a crab. During the chase the male uses the 'too-too too-too' note, similar to that heard in the display flight but repeated more slowly. Several 'pairs' may chase together and partners may be exchanged; a female may sit down and watch the antics of the other birds and another may join in. As pairs become established, the females are less likely to fly off, and the chases become longer. Wherever colour-marked birds have been involved, these chases have been between male and female. They are not in any way territorial. Sometimes the female will stop and allow the male to mount, but only for a few seconds. Near the time of egg laying, when the female stops, this initiates the wing-lifting ceremony during which copulation proper takes place.

Two to three weeks before egg laying, male Redshanks begin to scrape what are often referred to as 'false nests', 'cock-nests' or merely 'scrapes'. The male approaches a tuft, parts the blades with his bill and moves into its centre. He then lowers his breast on to the grass surface and rotates on his breast, whilst scratching backwards with his feet. The male will scrape for some five minutes until a circle of bare earth 8 to 10 cm (3 to 4 inches) across is exposed within the tuft. From just before entering the tuft, until leaving, the male utters a quiet 'song' a low-pitched 'tu-too-tu-too-tu-too-tu-too'; he then spends some time preening 1 to 2 metres (3 to 6 feet) from the scrape. Male Redshanks may produce 15 to 20 scrapes, but eventually show a preference for a particular one. Moving in and out of the scrape over a period of several days, the circle of bare earth is extended to some 14 to 15 cm (5½ to 6 inches) in diameter and scraping behaviour is interrupted by false brooding and grass-pulling over the scrape. Sometimes the female will approach the scraping male, enter the tuft and push the male out, but usually this happens only close to egg laying and the female does little or no scraping.

5. *An unusually open nest of a British Redshank. The brooding bird has a well marked breast but few breeding-plumage feathers on the mantle and back.*

At the end of a chase, an alighting ceremony takes place, or, when the female leaves the scrape, the male will often attempt the wing-lifting (pre-copulation) ceremony. The female holds her body in an almost horizontal position, with the wings slightly drooped and the white rump exposed. The male moves round to the front of the female, with head erect and body very upright, at the same time fanning his tail. The male's wings are then raised open above his back, so displaying the white underside to the female. The wings are waved slightly and then trembled until they are shaking violently; he approaches the female with a high, exaggerated stepping movement, using slow, short steps, like a soldier marking time. His bill is pointed to the ground, neck stretched a little, and all the while he sings with a continuous 'tloo tloo' note, the female responding with nervous 'tchips'. Within half a metre (18 inches) of the female the call note is changed to a gutteral 'cacacacaca', re-miniscent of the Lapwing's scraping note, and with the same undulating quality. The male's wings are beaten more rapid-ly, he becomes visibly more excited and, rising from the ground, he mounts the female and copulates. The male's calls become shriller and the display is ended only when he is dislodged from the female's back, whereupon he trills and she frequently gives a shrill squeal, fol-lowed by a burst of song. The pair then usually feed together for a time. Im-mediately prior to egg laying, copulation lasts some 8 to 9 seconds and wing-lifting up to 40 seconds. The first egg is usually laid within 30 hours of copulation.

Breeding

NESTING

Usually the first egg is laid on the bare earth exposed in the scrape by the male Redshank. The female selects the scrape from some fifteen or twenty which the male has produced in the early breeding season. Males scrape for some three to four weeks before laying takes place, so

the female usually has a wide range of possible nest sites, usually all within an area about 20 metres (22 yards) in dia-meter.

Because of the activity of the male, the scrapes are usually quite open when the first egg is laid. Favoured scrapes can often be identified before laying by the close presence of pellets. Sometimes a few grass stems and pieces of dead vegetation are pulled into the scrape before laying takes place, but usually first eggs can be found in open scrapes on bare earth. This makes them particularly sus-ceptible to predation: more nests contain-ing one egg are lost than those containing two or three eggs.

Whilst the female is laying, and subse-quently during incubation, she pulls more nesting material into the nest. This she arranges while sitting and also develops the canopy above her head. Males take part in both these activities since they share the incubation; by the time the clutch is completed the bower over the nest normally completely covers the eggs and shields them from the view of poten-tial predators. On the return of an in-cubating bird to the nest, after it has settled on the eggs, the next few minutes are spent rearranging the grass stems in a pyramid surrounding and covering the bird. Bird photographers thus have only a few seconds to take a shot, which prob-ably accounts for the relative dearth of good photographs of incubating Red-shanks in typical sites.

Usually Redshanks select marshy fields or water meadows inland, or occasionally they nest on rough moorland. In coastal areas, salt marshes are favoured nesting sites, particularly older marshes where *Festuca rubra* has developed. Here they nest along the channel edges, where, because of the levees produced by silt from the tide, the roots of vegetation are better aerated and the tufts are deeper. Occasionally nests are placed in more open areas, sometimes on shingle, but when this occurs they are usually placed next to a tussock or overhanging plant.

Where the typical canopy occurs over the nest, it tends to retain its shape and cover even when a bird is flushed from the nest. It has been recorded that incubating birds will rearrange the cover

7

6. *Roosting Redshanks at high tide in autumn; a colour-ringed bird from the Ribble is second from left.*

as they depart, but in most cases there is no need as the vegetation springs back as the bird leaves.

Redshanks tend to nest semi-colonially and during the breeding season do not appear to be territorial, nests sometimes being made only a metre or so apart. Inland, ten or a dozen pairs may be found nesting close together, with a distance of several kilometres before another group of nesting birds occurs. Often, between the two sites there is apparently suitable nesting habitat which is unoccupied; it is difficult to account for this breeding distribution of the species.

EGG LAYING AND INCUBATION

Eggs are laid at approximately 36-hour intervals, so the clutch is completed in about 4½ days. The last egg tends to be narrower and of smaller volume than the first three. The order of laying can often be established in completed clutches by the amount of mud on the eggs, the first being laid on bare earth, the second on some vegetation, the third on more nest material, and so forth. Incubation usually begins with the last egg and is shared

equally between male and female, though if one bird deserts or is killed, the other will continue incubation. Both male and female possess large brood patches and the nest is seldom left unoccupied during the incubation period, though the behaviour of individual birds varies markedly. Many Redshanks will leave their nests when a person approaches within 600 to 700 metres (660 to 770 yards), whilst others, particularly in the later stages of incubation, will sit tight and allow the observer to lift them off the nest.

The incubation period ranges between 22 and 31 days, though the longer periods are almost certainly the result of only a single bird incubating. Many factors affect the incubation period, of which climate is perhaps the most important: in cold, wet weather, incubation lasts longer. Frequent disturbance also affects the incubation period. On average, Redshanks nesting in salt marshes in the north of England incubate for some 25 days, but inland the period is shorter by some two days, and in the German Friesian Islands a mean of 23 days has

8

7. *A male Redshank prospecting for a suitable nesting site.*
8. *Male Redshank scraping.*

been recorded. Short incubation periods may to some extent be due to incubation beginning before the laying of the last egg, and longer periods in salt marsh habitats are caused by tidal disturbance. There is no particular pattern of male and female incubation, though individual birds of either sex usually seem to prefer incubating at set times of the day. It is unusual for the eggs to be left altogether at the changeover; one bird may physically push its mate off the nest in order to take its place incubating.

The clutch size in Redshanks is almost invariably four, though occasionally three occurs, in most cases because one egg has been 'laid away'. Sometimes an odd egg is laid in a nearby scrape. Clutches of more than four eggs are often due to two females laying in the same nest, but occasionally five and even six eggs can be produced at one laying. Where a clutch is lost early in incubation, this is often replaced within eight to twelve days; Redshanks can produce three full clutches in a season when necessary.

Laying normally begins towards the end of April and usually experienced breeders lay first, with birds breeding for the first time laying on average a fortnight later. In salt marsh breeders season is often artificially extended by losses to high tides and laying can take place as late as the middle of July, though such clutches are almost invariably deserted.

HATCHING AND CHICK DEVELOPMENT

In inland populations in Britain and in salt marsh populations unaffected by tidal inundation, hatching may take place at the end of the second week or in the third week of May. All eggs begin to chip simultaneously, and in normal circumstances all four chicks hatch within a few hours of each other. Shells are usually carried away by the adult birds and, as soon as the young are dry, they may be led away from the nest. However, if hatching takes place at night, they usually remain in the nest until daylight.

At the time of hatching the amount of nest material is much greater than at the time of laying, as material is added to the nest throughout incubation. Signs of a successful hatch can always be found amongst the nesting material in the form of shell fragments. If, for any reason, eggs fail to hatch, or if one chick takes much longer than the others to emerge, they are deserted by the parents, who lead the dry, hatched chicks to a suitable feeding area.

Inland, such journeys are often extensive and families may negotiate several hazards on the way. Chicks and adults are quite capable of swimming and may walk distances in excess of 2 km (1¼ miles) within a few hours of hatching. When major obstacles are encountered, such as walls or vertical river banks, adults will carry young across them. As with the Woodcock, Redshank young are carried singly between the legs, up against the belly, and in this way adults can fly whilst carrying a chick.

Usually both parents are in attendance when chicks leave the nest, but one parent, usually the female, may desert the family within a few days, leaving the mate to tend the chicks until fledging. Sometimes a family will split up, each adult taking one or more chicks. The chicks are able to feed themselves as soon as they leave the nest and are never fed by adults. In cold weather and at night, they are brooded by the adults, until at about ten days old they are able to maintain their own body temperatures. Brooding is then less frequent but may occur at night until fledging. During the fledging period (and immediately before the hatch) the adults are very demonstrative, though they are less so near the time of fledging.

Young Redshanks are able to fly at about 25 days, though in many cases do not do so until between 28 and 30 days after the hatch. At this stage they still weigh less than 100 grams (3½ ounces) and in flight are noticeably smaller than adults. Mortality during the fledging period is high: usually only a single chick will survive to fledging and many broods are lost entirely.

Occasionally a pair may be double-brooded and there are records of the female of a pair laying whilst chicks of the first brood were still alive. There are, however, no records of Redshanks fledging two broods in a season.

10

PAIR FORMATION

Redshanks are very faithful to their mates; a pair is usually maintained until the death of one or the other. Divorces take place mainly when breeding is unsuccessful, but even when a pair changes mates during a particular breeding season, it may well re-pair the following season. Where a male loses his mate, a new female is usually attracted to the same nesting area, but where a female loses a mate she normally lays in an area where her new mate is scraping. Where a pair is maintained from year to year, the nest site selected may be identical throughout, down to the same tuft of grass.

Redshanks may not breed until the second or third year of life, but are capable of doing so in the first year. There is one record of a female ten months old incubating a full clutch. However, the normal age at first breeding is probably two years. Birds may live for up to fifteen years, though three to four is probably the normal lifespan.

Feeding

In winter, the large majority of Redshanks feed on the shore or in channels and gutters on the salt marsh. Here they take a variety of invertebrates but those most commonly ingested are the burrowing shrimp *Corophium,* the marine snail *Hydrobia,* ragworms and small crabs. These animals are also taken in summer by coastal nesting Redshanks. At this time they also take insects from the surface of the salt marsh and, inland, insects and insect larvae play an important part in the diet.

Watching feeding Redshanks, it is often difficult to identify food items or to see whether they take an item at all. *Corophium* is taken below the surface of the mud and often swallowed with little change in the steady progression of the bird, but ragworms and crabs are more obvious prey. On occasions, Redshanks will wade for food and take shrimps and small fish, but generally food items are

9. Newly hatched chicks before leaving the nest.

10. *A Spanish breeding Redshank approaching the nest.*
11. *A Norwegian Redshank (Tringa totanus totanus) in breeding plumage.*

12. *A brooding British Redshank showing some winter feathers.*
13. *Redshank's nest with covering canopy moved to one side.*

small and unrecognisable. Identification is made more difficult by Redshanks usually swallowing their food whole; however, they produce pellets which contain the hard parts of the prey.

Pellets may be found commonly on the surface of the mud on which Redshanks have been feeding, or on the salt marsh where they have roosted. Examination of pellets shows them to contain hard parts of *Corophium* and crabs, shells of molluscs and chaetae from polychaete worms, which clearly demonstrates that Redshanks have been eating these animals. However, sometimes Redshanks will eat the flesh of molluscs without taking in the shell, for example *Cardium* (cockles) which have been damaged by other birds or fishermen, and this cannot be deduced from pellets. Usually close observation from a hide is the only reliable method of observing the nature and frequency of intake of food items, as pellet examination gives a biased view of food intake due to differences in digestibility and times and places of collection. It has been shown, however, from pellet collection that *Hydrobia* is a more important prey species in October to April and *Carcinus* from May to October, with *Corophium* being taken most often in June.

In an elegant series of studies, Dr John Goss-Custard has examined the winter feeding of the Redshank in relation to the distribution of its prey. He found that the density of feeding Redshanks was positively correlated with the density of *Corophium*; in other words, where there were more *Corophium,* there were more Redshanks, and feeding was more efficient in areas of high prey biomass. However, there is a density of prey at which predation rate levels off, and this is much lower than might be expected: around 1000 per square metre. However, the intake of *Corophium* still increases at higher densities, because the Redshanks then select large individual prey items.

During severe weather, Redshanks are the first species of wader to be affected, and in heavy frosts many are found dead on the tideline. This is not because food is not present, but because they are unable to reach it; feeding high on the shore they normally find their food in areas which are first to be frozen over. As tempera-tures fall, so the feeding behaviour of Redshanks changes. Above 6 C (43 F) *Corophium* is a preferred prey, but below this temperature more *Macoma* (a bivalve mollusc) and ragworms are taken. This may be due to the behaviour of the invertebrates at lower temperature, rather than a change in preference by the birds.

Work carried out on the food requirements of Redshanks suggests that, even though they spend most of the daylight hours feeding, in winter they take in less than their total food requirements during the day. Like many waders, Redshanks will feed at night and, particularly in winter, they may need to do so in order to obtain sufficient food. At night Redshanks take more *Hydrobia* than during the day, possibly because they have more difficulty locating *Corophium* in their burrows.

The daily intake of food in a Redshank is of the order of 30 per cent of its weight, or in the course of a year some 19.7 kg (43 pounds). In spring, when Redshanks begin to take in more insect material and a smaller quantity of marine invertebrates, they are able to obtain their energy intake more quickly as insect material has a higher calorific equivalent per gram of dry weight. Like most waders wintering in Europe, Redshanks have a midwinter peak of fat content, when some 16 per cent of the body weight is made up of fat. From then on there is usually a decline in weight, as fat is used up, until the end of March, when another increase in weight takes place as birds come into breeding condition. The fat serves two purposes, as insulation and as a food reserve: Redshanks found dead in hard weather have usually lost their fat.

Plumages and moults

On hatching, the chicks normally dry within a few hours and leave the nest. At this time they are covered with down and remain completely downy until some 4½ days old, when pins appear on the flanks and scapulars. Feather development

14

takes place first in the areas most important for insulation and flight, so that the flanks, breast, belly and mantle, together with the wings and tail, develop feathers before the underside of the wing. The feathers first emerge from the pins on the breast after eight days and it is also the breast feathers that are the first to emerge fully at about thirteen days. Wings and tail feathers are not fully emerged until about three weeks after hatching, but there is considerable variation in timing of emergence of all feathers, so the degree of feather emergence is not a good aging characteristic. At ten days old, a chick weighs roughly 40 grams (1½ ounces), at fifteen days 60 grams (2¼ ounces), at twenty days 80 grams (3 ounces) and at twenty-five days 100 grams (3½ ounces).

The first plumage the downy chick moults into is the juvenile plumage. This is characterised by dark brown feathers with extensive buff fringes, giving birds a mottled appearance on the upper parts. The breast is spotted with much paler and less clearly defined markings than the adult summer birds and the belly is white. This plumage is retained only until the first September of life and then the post-juvenile moult gives rise to the first winter plumage. None of the flight feathers are replaced at this moult, which is confined to the body feathers, some or all of the tail feathers, some innermost secondaries and some wing coverts. First-winter birds can be recognised by the retention of juvenile wing coverts and sometimes by the tertiaries and central tail feathers (pointed in juvenile plumage) being retained.

The moult into first-winter plumage produces a paler and more uniformly marked bird, lacking the mottled appearance of the juvenile. All the body feathers on the upper parts are uniformly ash brown, though the rachis of some feathers may be darker. The breast is white, with some grey suffusion at the sides of certain British and Icelandic birds; there is a little barring on the belly and under tail coverts. This plumage is retained until the spring of the following year, when under normal circumstances a full body moult takes place.

In the northern Scandinavian breeding birds that winter in Africa, and in the populations from the east of the range, the spring moult begins in March. When birds arrive back in the breeding areas they normally possess a full breeding plumage but retain the flight feathers and tail feathers which were assumed at the autumn moult. In the breeding plumage the breast feathers are spotted and the feathers of the mantle and back, together with those of the scapulars and tertiaries, are richly marked in two colours, dependent upon the populations in question: dark brown and grey-buff in the Scandinavian and Himalayan birds (*Tringa totanus totanus* and *T. t. eurhinus*), and various degrees of dark brown and cinnamon in the other populations (*T. t. ussuriensis, T. t. craggi* and *T. t. terrignotae*).

Some individuals have a full moult and others do not moult at all in spring. Even in a full winter plumage birds seem to have little difficulty finding a mate, and birds with a full breeding plumage in Britain have no demonstrable advantage.

In the first breeding season some birds retain feathers from the juvenile plumage, particularly on the wing coverts and the tertiaries. Their absence, however, does not mean that the bird is in its second year, as some first-year birds make a full moult in the first autumn of life. The degree of wear of the primaries is also an indication of age, as first-year birds retain the flight feathers from the juvenile plumage whilst second-year birds have flight feathers produced at the first post-nuptial moult, which may have been completed only the previous November. Thus, flight feathers in second-year birds may have been in use for only half the period of time of those of a first-year bird, which may have reached full growth in the previous July.

There is more variety in the plumage of the Redshank than in any other wader, particularly in birds occurring in Britain. Even in winter the degree of darker markings in the region of the rachis of feathers on the upper parts is variable in both British and Icelandic birds, and the spring moult produces birds which range from those retaining a full winter plumage to those few with a full breeding plumage. There is such variety that indi-

14. *Redshank chicks, newly hatched.*

viduals can be easily recognised without colour marking (though in any population study it is wise to have individuals marked).

Distribution and taxonomy

In winter one Redshank looks very like another, but in Britain, in spring and summer, no two birds look alike. This has resulted in numerous subspecies being proposed, for several of which there are no good grounds, but the variation gives clues to how populations have evolved and how Redshanks have come to inhabit the different parts of Eurasia in the breeding season and some populations other parts of the world in winter.

The Redshank breeds throughout western and central Europe and eastwards across Asia to the coast of the eastern USSR. In the west it breeds as far north as northern Norway and the Kola peninsula but its breeding range drops to latitude 60°N in the Urals and to 53°N in the eastern USSR. In the south it breeds in Tunisia, Spain, sporadically in the northern Mediterranean, in Turkestan, Kashmir, Tibet, western China and Mongolia. Since it occurs right across the Old World it is not surprising that different populations show variations in morphology; ten different races have been described in the literature. However, there is little justification for several of these; and the present writer revised the taxonomy of the species in 1971.

The British birds are of particular interest in that in general they do not assume a full breeding plumage in spring. A separate race, *Tringa totanus britannica* Mathews 1935, was erected on the basis of this character, but the subspecies could not be maintained as Icelandic Redshanks also have this character, albeit to a smaller extent. The Icelandic Redshank, *T. t. robusta* (Schioler) 1919, is, on average, a bigger bird than the British Redshank and possesses more breeding plumage. Where breeding plumage occurs the feathers are tinted

16

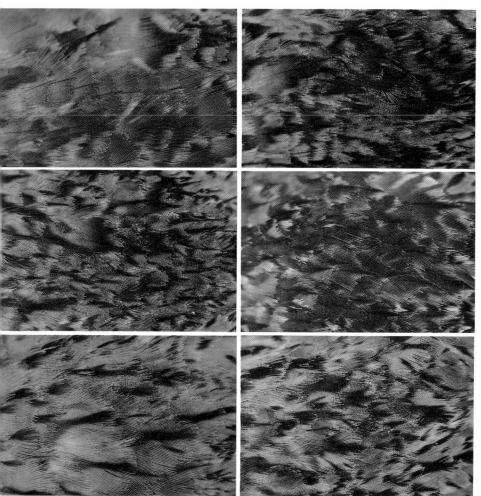

15. *Colour variation in the mantle across the range of the Redshank: (top left) Iceland (Tringa totanus robusta) showing retained winter feathers; (top right) eastern USSR (T. t. ussuriensis) showing full breeding plumage; (middle left) northern Scandinavia (T. t. totanus), light phase; (middle right) northern Scandinavia (T. t. totanus), dark phase, very similar to T. t. eurhinus; (bottom left) Lop Nor, China (T. t. craggi); (bottom right) eastern China (T. t. terrignotae).*

buff-cinnamon. The so-called 'Continental' Redshank, *T. t. totanus* (L.) 1785, is a smaller bird than either the British or Icelandic Redshanks; it occurs in two colour forms: a dark brown, chocolate-coloured bird with heavy breast spotting and a paler, greyer bird, again heavily marked. These colour forms occur and breed together in northern Scandinavia and possibly Spain; both usually have a full breeding plumage, lacking buff-cinnamon feathers in spring and summer.

To the east of the Urals birds occur which have a full breeding plumage and buff-cinnamon feathers. This form extends to the eastern coast of the USSR and into Japan; it is named *T. t. ussuriensis* Buturlin 1934. To the west of the Urals, right across central Europe, the birds are mainly like the 'Continental' Redshanks but are very variable in the amount of breeding plumage they assume in spring. A similar situation occurs in the Tian Shan region, north of India. In northern Kashmir and Tibet, dark brown birds occur, which are bigger but morphologically similar to those of northern Scandinavia. These form a good subspecies, *T. t. eurhinus* Oberholster 1900.

Two other colour forms exist, a very cinnamon-coloured bird from eastern China (*T. t. terrignotae* Meinertzhagen 1926) and a red form, only a single specimen of which is known from the breeding range (*T. t. craggi* Hale 1971).

How did all these colour forms arise? It is likely that the main ones (*totanus, eurhinus, ussuriensis, terrignotae, craggi*) were at one time geographically separate populations, with little or no gene flow between them. They had not remained as separate populations for sufficiently long to become separate species, but they had become subspecies. There is some evidence for this.

There are two parts of the breeding range where buff-cinnamon coloured birds (*ussuriensis*) meet brown birds (*totanus* and *eurhinus*), in central Europe and north of India (Tian Shan). In both areas there are populations of birds which do not acquire a full breeding plumage and have the characteristics of hybrid swarms in that colour forms from other parts of the range of the species occur within them.

The dimorphism of the 'Continental' Redshank, *T. t. totanus*, has not always been as it is now. Before 1910 only the brown form was present in northern Scandinavia. Redshanks in the supposed hybrid zones are bigger birds than those occurring there prior to hybridisation, for which the increase in size affords further evidence. Since 1910, and coincident with the spread of grey birds into northern Scandinavia, average size has increased; the grey birds may well be associated with hybridisation and possibly a result of it. This may help to date the time of hybridisation in western Europe as post-1910.

ORIGINS OF THE COLOUR FORMS

It is interesting to speculate on how the present populations of different colour forms might have arisen. Towards the end of the last glaciation, some 20,000 years BP, most of the present breeding range would have been unoccupied by Redshanks. Previous Redshank populations had been pushed by the ice to refuges in the south. It is likely that the Redshanks of the Mediterranean and northern India were isolated in refuges at approximately A and B on figure 16 (or this may have been a single refuge); these were the dark brown birds. Buff-cinnamon birds (*ussuriensis*) were probably isolated in refuge C. Alternatively, they may not have diverged morphologically until this separation.

Consequent upon the melt of the ice the population of brown birds (*eurhinus*) in B moved north and the buff-cinnamon birds from refuge C spread westwards, a movement that many waders with origins in China have made during their evolution. Brown birds from refuge A moved north, eventually to colonise northern Scandinavia. During this process, *ussuriensis* from the east met *eurhinus* from the south in the region of Tian Shan (north of India), where secondary hybridisation took place, forming the first hybrid swarm. More northerly *ussuriensis,* still moving westwards, contacted the dark brown *totanus* west of the Urals and secondary hybridisation again took place. The westward spread of *ussuriensis,* or at least the central European hybrids, continued into Britain and Iceland. This left the whole of central Europe west of the Urals, Britain, Iceland and a geographically separate area in Tian Shan populated by hybrid Redshanks, with non-hybrid brown birds remaining in the Himalayas and Scandinavia, and buff-cinnamon birds east of the Urals.

In the centre of both hybrid zones the birds are intermediate in size between the parent populations, but in western Europe they are significantly larger than the original brown birds and increase in size as they extend west from the centre of hybridisation, being largest in Iceland. Almost certainly present-day selection plays a large part in the size of Redshanks in Iceland, though the hybrid birds, being

18

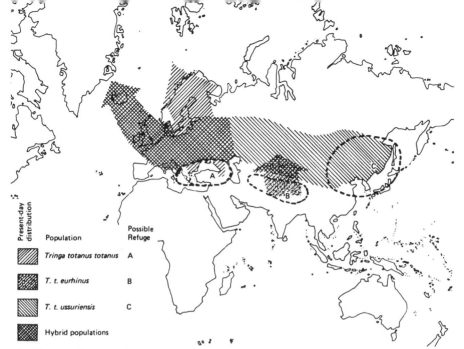

16. *The spread westwards of Tringa totanus ussuriensis showing hybrid zones and probable areas of origin of parent populations.*

larger in the first place (which probably enabled them to colonise Iceland) were good material on which selection could operate.

Icelandic, British and Russian birds from east of the Urals (*ussuriensis*) all have dark cinnamon breeding plumage feathers (when breeding plumage is assumed) and form an east-west cline of increasing size from Japan to Iceland, there being an interruption in size increase in the central European hybrid zone. This cline is best known as the *T. t. ussuriensis x robusta* cline, and any division of it must be arbitrary. Hence, the British Redshank, occurring in the middle of a cline, is not a good subspecies.

Specimens of Redshanks taken in Spain during the breeding season are very similar to northern Scandinavian birds; both grey and dark brown forms occur there. Evidence for the Spanish birds originally being non-hybrid is provided by figure 10, which is of a small, dark Spanish bird at the nest.

Throughout the distribution of the species there is a large range in size, from a mean wing length of 153.5 ± 1.48 mm (6.04 $\pm$ 0.35 inches) in male *T. t. ussuriensis* to 170.4 $\pm$ 0.76 mm (6.71 $\pm$ 0.18 inches) in female *T. t. robusta;* the latter may be up to twice the weight of the former. Bergmann's Rule states that, in warm-blooded animals, those members of a species in the north of the range tend to be larger than those in the south. This is because large animals have a smaller surface area/volume ratio and, therefore, lose heat less readily than smaller forms. In the Redshank some of the smaller forms (*T. t. totanus* males, prior to 1910, had a mean wing length of 155.6 ± 3.2 mm, 6.13 ± 0.13 inches) occur furthest north, in northern Scandinavia. This may seem a contradiction, but, on examining the migratory habits of different populations, it can be seen to fit the general thesis of the rule. As complex as the taxonomy of the species are its migrations, where some populations move not at all and others thousands of miles.

19

17. *Juvenile and winter plumage at high tide; the fourth bird from left is in juvenile plumage.*

Migrations

Redshanks are common birds on the coastline of Britain throughout the year, though many of those present in the winter are not British birds, but visitors from Iceland. Some British birds move on to Europe but the migrations performed by these populations are small in comparison with those made by Scandinavian birds.

There are few ringing records outside western Europe, and in the case of Scandinavian birds the recorded distances are gross underestimates of the journeys the birds make, as there is little chance of ringing recoveries from south of the equator. Of the western European populations of the Redshank, the northern Scandinavian birds are smaller and lighter in weight than any of the others; it is, therefore, of some interest that they perform the longest migrations. Danish and German birds move no further than North Africa for winter, and many stay in the area of the breeding grounds. The Norwegian and Swedish birds overfly these populations in their migrations and are said to perform a 'leap-frog' migra-

tion. In winter, the populations of the smallest and least heavy birds are, therefore, in the south of the range and the largest and heaviest (Icelandic birds) in the north, with birds intermediate in size and weight in between.

Figure 18 shows the wintering areas of Redshank in western Europe and, in the left-hand margin, the mean wing length of male birds (size), as measured in the breeding areas of those populations. It has been argued that, since the smallest birds occur in the south of the winter range, and the largest ones in the north, this fits in well with Bergmann's Rule and size has been selected for in the winter range. Both these conclusions are supportable as long as it is assumed that the wintering areas are occupied only by those populations from the breeding grounds of western Europe. On measuring wintering birds, this was found not to be the case: winter birds from the eastern Mediterranean were found to be as big as those from central England, and birds from east Africa bigger than those from northern Africa. These measurements are shown on figure 18: clearly Africa is occupied in winter by Redshanks which breed elsewhere than in western Europe. Large and small Redshanks winter together in much of Africa, so it is

20

unlikely that selection for size takes place in winter. Further evidence for varying sizes of Redshanks wintering together might be found if information existed on the migration of Redshanks breeding outside western Europe.

Museum collections contain many specimens of Redshanks taken outside the breeding season; on a basis of their measurements it was found possible to attribute individuals to known breeding populations using a simple computer program. This was done on the basis of five measurements: wing length, tail length, tarsus length, tarsus width and bill length, separately for adult males, adult females, first-year males and first-year females. The program gave the three most likely areas of origin from 31 possible breeding populations. In the case of

adult birds the computer allocations were surprisingly good in that the first allocation usually provided a very probable area of origin. In areas where a comparison was possible between real ringing recoveries and 'computer recoveries' (for example, the British Isles and Iceland), a close match was obtained between the two methods, so for areas outside western Europe 'computer recoveries' might be considered to give an overall picture of wintering areas. A further test of the method was provided by calculating the mean distances of recovery; here too there was a close match between ringing and 'computer recoveries'. Since these results were published, a Redshank ringed in the Philippines was recovered in the Ussuri Valley in the eastern USSR, which is the area predicted by the computer

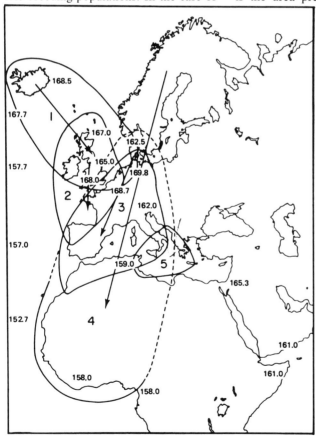

18. *The wintering areas of western European populations of Redshanks.*

21

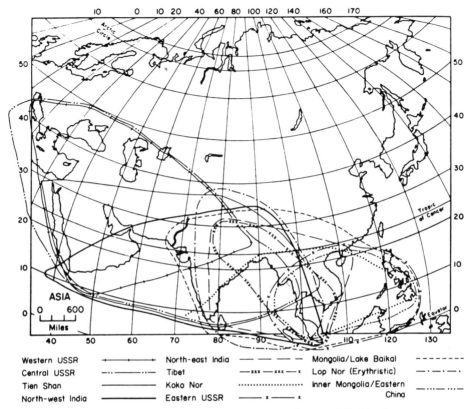

Western USSR	+—+—+	North-east India	— — — —
Central USSR	—··—··	Tibet	—xxx—xxx—x
Tien Shan	———	Koko Nor	················
North-west India	———	Eastern USSR	— x —— x
		Mongolia/Lake Baikal	– – – –
		Lop Nor (Erythristic)	—·—·—·
		Inner Mongolia/Eastern China	—··—··—

19. *The wintering areas of the more eastern breeding populations of Redshanks.*

program.

On the whole, Redshanks tend to winter directly to the south of their breeding areas, though there are considerable movements east and west, presumably to reach coastal or other wet wintering areas. This is shown in figure 19. Over most of the range of the species, migrant Redshanks make journeys of between 1500 and 3000 miles (2400 - 4800 km) from the breeding grounds to the wintering areas. Young birds tend to travel even further, so it is clear that British, Icelandic and central European birds are exceptional in making only short migratory journeys. Those that do so come from the presumed hybrid populations; hybridisation seems to have resulted in larger individuals which no longer need to migrate to any great extent.

Examination of wintering populations of Redshanks from right across the range suggests that there is no relationship between size and wintering latitude, as might be deduced from considering only the western European birds (figure 18). In the Philippines and the Malay peninsula both the largest Redshanks, from northern India and Tian Shan, and the smallest, from the eastern USSR, winter alongside each other; in the Persian Gulf small birds from Finland and the Kola peninsula winter with the birds from the central USSR which are as big as Icelandic birds. It seems unlikely that, within the same species, two separate breeding populations would have a character such as size selected in different directions in the same winter environment.

Consideration of the pattern of size

22

distribution in the breeding season shows that there is an east-west cline of increasing size from the eastern USSR to the Urals, which is then apparently interfered with by the hybridisation with the small brown Scandinavian birds, only to increase again in Iceland. However, there is a close correlation between size and the minimum recorded May temperature across the whole of the range, which suggests that the measurements are selected for, and not entirely a result of, hybridisation.

The northern Scandinavian birds are the only population that does not appear to fit this pattern. Ringing recoveries have shown that the northern Scandinavian birds return to the breeding ground some four weeks later than British and Danish birds; if June temperatures are substituted for May ones, there is a close fit with the regression line (figure 20).

It seems likely, therefore, that size (wing length) in Redshanks is selected for on the breeding ground and not in the winter range, and Bergmann's Rule is obeyed only in summer. Many species of birds contain both migratory and non-migratory populations but few show the complexities found in the Redshank, which seem to result from hybridisation of previously separated populations.

Populations

With the draining of wetlands, the Redshank populations of Europe in general have declined over the past century, though there is evidence to suggest that Britain and Iceland have maintained their breeding populations and possibly increased them. Estimates of the breeding population of Britain and Ireland range from 38,000 to 48,000 pairs; in Europe this is exceeded only by Norway where some 58,000 pairs are estimated to breed. In the south of the range Spain has about 4,000 breeding pairs and Tunisia 200 to 250 pairs.

Estimates for wintering populations suggest that the breeding populations may have been underestimated. A figure of approximately 115,000 in Britain and Ireland suggests a breeding population of over 60,000 for Iceland, which is probably excessive. With estimates of over 110,000 wintering in Atlantic Africa, 13,000 in Holland, and 12,000 in the Mediterranean, either very large numbers must be moving eastwards from central Europe and Asia, or breeding populations have been underestimated.

It is very easy to underestimate a

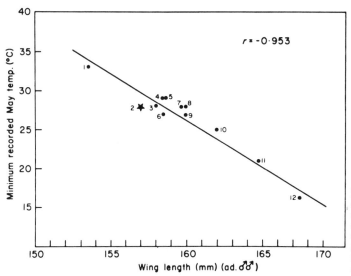

20. *The relationship between wing length and minimum recorded May temperatures; point 2 is northern Sweden at minimum recorded June temperatures.*

23

breeding population of Redshanks: merely counting demonstrative birds is not a good method. On the Ribble marshes it is possible to walk across a specific area and see fewer than twenty birds in an area where some two hundred nests are to be found. (Despite the Redshank being such a noisy bird it avoids publicising its presence when breeding.)

The oldest Redshank on record is a ringing recovery of a seventeen-year-old bird, but breeding for fourteen years has been recorded in some individuals. A pair of Redshanks need produce only two young which become adult during their own lifetimes in order to maintain the population numbers. Therefore, for a female breeding for fourteen years, and probably laying 56 eggs, 54 of them effectively make no contribution to the population, assuming numbers remain steady. There is, thus, a high level of mortality, of which there have been several different estimates.

On a salt marsh habitat the egg losses vary greatly from year to year. In a poor year hardly any may hatch, whilst in a good year almost three chicks per nest might be expected. A five-year average for the 1970s gives 0.65 chicks per nest, so during this time fewer than one-sixth of the eggs laid produced chicks. Prefledging mortality of chicks is of the order of 70 per cent; juvenile mortality from fledging to one year old is approximately 40 per cent. At the end of the first year, from every hundred eggs laid in previous years, fewer than three birds (2.9) are still alive to enter the breeding population.

Calculations of adult mortality from ringing recoveries have given annual mortality rates of the order of 43 per cent. This figure is much greater than that calculated from breeding studies in Britain and Germany, which have both produced an estimate of less than 25 per cent annual adult mortality; there appears to be no difference between male and female adult mortality.

Little is known of how population sizes of wading birds are regulated. It is probable that this is via density-dependent mortality factors which act more severely on high-density populations. Most mortality occurs in winter, but this is not density-dependent and regulation probably occurs on the breeding grounds. Redshanks are not territorial and competition for nest sites is not a likely method of regulating numbers. Where territoriality occurs, this is one way of limiting competition for food once the young have hatched, so it may be that, where territoriality does not exist, competition for food is great.

On hatching, Redshank chicks are led to suitable feeding areas by their parents. In dry seasons, such feeding areas may be few in number and there may be competition for them. With a limited number of suitable feeding sites, mortality will be more severe at high densities than at low densities and thus mortality will be density-dependent. The difficulty of estimating fledging success in waders makes this a difficult hypothesis to test but one worth examining in the future.

The more one becomes familiar with any topic, the more problems appear. The study of Redshanks is no exception to this general rule: there is plenty left to find out about one of the most fascinating birds.

Further reading

Cramp, S., and Simmons, K. E. L. *Handbook of the Birds of Europe, the Middle East and North Africa,* volume 3. Oxford University Press, 1983.
Hale, W. G. *Waders.* Collins, 1980.
Stiefel, A., and Sheufler, H. *Der Rotschenkel.* A Ziemsen Verlag, Wittenberg Lutherstadt, 1984.

ACKNOWLEDGEMENTS
The author wishes to thank Eric and David Hosking for the cover picture and photographs 5, 6, 9, 10, 11, 12, 17.